Juniper of WANDERWOOD

Library of Congress Control Number 2024910137

ISBN 979-8-9896630-0-2

First edition 2024
Wanderwood Media Group
Plantation, Florida
Inqueries: Jennifer@wanderwoodmediagroup.com

Follow us on Instagram: @JuniperofWanderwood
Facebook: Juniper of Wanderwood

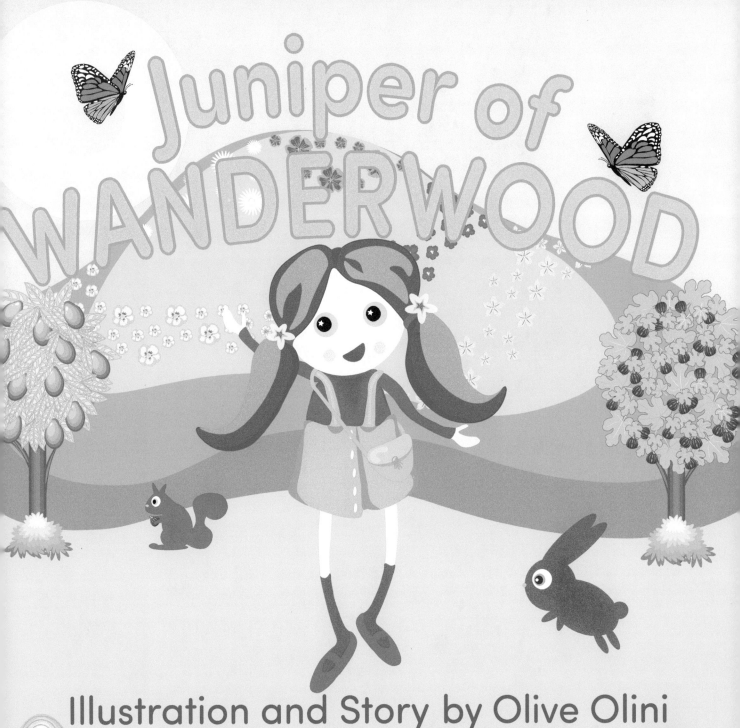

Juniper of WANDERWOOD

Illustration and Story by Olive Olini

Wanderwood Media Group

Blueberry Bunny felt awfully blue. Everything that he saw had a dull gray hue.

"Oh, where should I go, and what should I do?
My step has no bounce, and I haven't a clue."
So he wandered the streets, and alleyways, too,
'Til he found a path to somewhere brand new.

Not far up the path, in her cheery room,
Juniper Berry awoke to a tune.
"Birds, do you sing lullabies to the moon?
So brightly you croon, you chase off the gloom!"

And shaking off sleep like dust from a broom,
She left her house - not a moment too soon.

When Juniper reached the spot where he stood,
Bunny grew nervous, as he often would.
"I've never been anywhere quite this good,
Do Bunnies belong in this neighborhood?"

WANDERWOOD

Juniper answered, "It's well understood
That we *all* have a place in Wanderwood!"

So now that they'd met and said their hellos,
they went for a walk where the jasmine grows.
"If you take a whiff, you'll forget your woes.
It's like dancing on air with twinkly toes!

Let's follow that bee to see where he goes,
But give him his space,
Don't follow too close!"

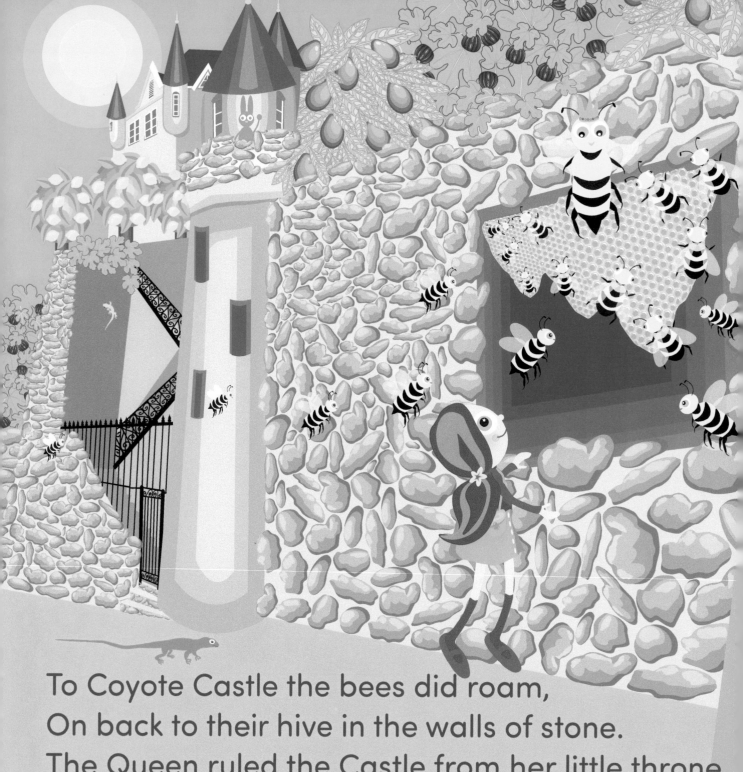

To Coyote Castle the bees did roam,
On back to their hive in the walls of stone.
The Queen ruled the Castle from her little throne,

And bossed around bees in the honeycomb.
She invited her guests into her home,
"Explore the estate like it was your own."

Through the Queen's gardens they quietly strolled
And soon discovered a sight to behold –
The wonderful gifts Mother Nature bestowed,

Like lemons and oranges as precious as gold.
Bunny cheered, "We've struck the mother lode!
I'm so excited that I could I explode!"

While hummingbirds, bees,
And butterflies swooped,
And chattering squirrels had heated disputes,
Bunny and Juniper harvested fruits –

Avocados and figs from branches that drooped.
Hurry up, chickens, get back to the coop,
Snappy Coyote is out for a snoop!

Returning to roost, feeling safe and sound,
The chickens goofed off like a bunch of clowns.
While they strutted their stuff and scratched the
ground,

Juniper noticed the sun going down.
"It's time to go home, we better turn 'round,
Wild things come out after dark in this town!"

Beneath the gaze of the Watchful Owl,
All the night creatures went out on the prowl.
The sight of a skunk made Juniper scowl,
"Slinky the Skunk is cute, but he's foul!"
Then Juniper's tummy began to growl,
And Snappy got scared and started to howl!

Now back at Juniper's, they prepared food.
They measured, chopped, blended, stirred,
Simmered and stewed.

When dinner was ready, they "Aaahhh'ed," and they "Ooohhh'ed,"
Then they ate so fast that they barely chewed!
Yummy dessert further sweetened their mood,
And their hearts overflowed with gratitude!

Shakin' Lavender Lemonade
4 servings

1/2 tablespoon lavender
1/2 cup fresh squeezed lemon juice
1/2 cup maple syrup
water
pinch of salt
2 32 oz Mason jars (one with a with plastic lid)

Overnight lavender infusion
Place 1/2 tablespoon of lavender into a 32 oz mason jar fill with boiling water. Place lid on and let steep overnight. Strain the infusion in the morning.

In another mason jar combine 1/2 cup lemon juice, 1/2 a cup of maple syrup, 1 cup of the strained lavender infusion, a pinch of salt and 1 1/2 cups of water. Place plastic lid on and shake, shake, shake.
Serve over ice.

You can make any adjustments to flavor based on preferences.

The leftover strained lavender infusion can be consumed as a calming tea.

Creamy Curry Orangey Carroty Soup

servings

cup of orange juice and zest
tablespoons of olive oil
pproximately 2 pounds of carrots chopped
cups of vegetable broth
cup of coconut milk
shallots sliced
garlic cloves sliced
tablespoon mild curry (optional, if the curry powder is not labeled mild it
will have a bit of a kick from cayenne pepper)
/4 teaspoon of salt and 1/4 teaspoon pepper (adjust to your tastes)
Optional toppings: fresh chives and homemade croutons (bread and olive
il)

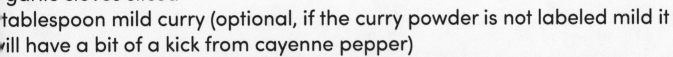

eat the olive oil in a large pan on medium low heat. Add the shallots and
arlic. Let the shallots and garlic soften and become translucent for about
-5 minutes. If using curry powder add to the shallot/ garlic mixture, allow
o cook for another minute. Add the carrots and orange zest, cook for about
more minutes. Add three cups of broth and 1 cup of coconut milk, bring to
slow boil, turn heat down to low and simmer for 20-30 minutes (stovetop
emperatures vary), check the softness of the carrots.

Once the fork penetrates the carrots nicely it is time to transfer all
ngredients to a high power blender and blend until creamy. Stir in the
range juice and viola, soup is on. Season to taste with salt and
epper.

Minty Avocado sauce over roasted cauliflower

4 servings

Sauce
1 avocado
3/4 cup of fresh mint leaves
2 tablespoons of maple syrup
Juice of two limes
1 tablespoon of olive oil
1 tablespoon of water

Cauliflower
2 tbsp. olive oil
1 head of cauliflower
 chopped into small florets
salt to taste

Possible side options Pearl Couscous, Quinoa, superfood blend or rice
Sauce
Combine all of the sauce ingredients in a blender and blend until smooth. You can add more water if too thick but add a little at a time so the sauce doesn't become too runny.

Cauliflower
Preheat the oven to 400 degrees. Mix the cauliflower in a bowl with 2 tablespoons of olive oil and a pinch of salt. Roast for approximately 30 minutes flipping halfway through the process. Oven times may vary so keep an eye on on the cauliflowers to make sure they get nicely roasted but not overdone.
Plate the cauliflower over your choice of side options (Pearl Couscous, Quinoa, superfood blend or rice(Juniper prefers Pearl CousCous) and top with the sauce.

Figgy-Orangey pudding
4 servings

8oz figs (figs can be substituted with strawberries or segmented oranges)
8oz a non-dairy coconut based yogurt
1 1/2 table spoons of maple syrup
1 orange and zest
1/4 teaspoon cinnamon powder
Optional garnish mint leaves

Pudding-In a bowl mix yogurt, 3/4 teaspoon of orange zest, 1 tablespoon of maple syrup, 1/4 teaspoon of cinnamon powder, and two tablespoons of fresh orange juice.

Figgy topping- Quarter the figs (strawberries or oranges). Mix the fruit with 1/4 teaspoon of zest, 1/2 a tablespoon of maple syrup, and an 1/8 cup of orange juice.

Place the pudding in a serving bowl, top with fruit and enjoy.

Optional: garnish with chopped mint leaves.

Printed in the USA
CPSIA information can be obtained
at www.ICGtesting.com
LVHW072136210624
783275LV00002B/3